To

JP

With thanks to
Annie Simpson and Karen Morrison.

Copyright © 2009

make believe ideas

The Wilderness, Berkhamsted,
Hertfordshire, HP4 2AZ, UK.

10 Little Penguins

make
believe
ideas

ready for some fun . . .

way before the day's begun.

Search me!

9 playful penguins are

1 penguin eats too fast and now has tummy ache!

Oh dear!

6

happy penguins, all

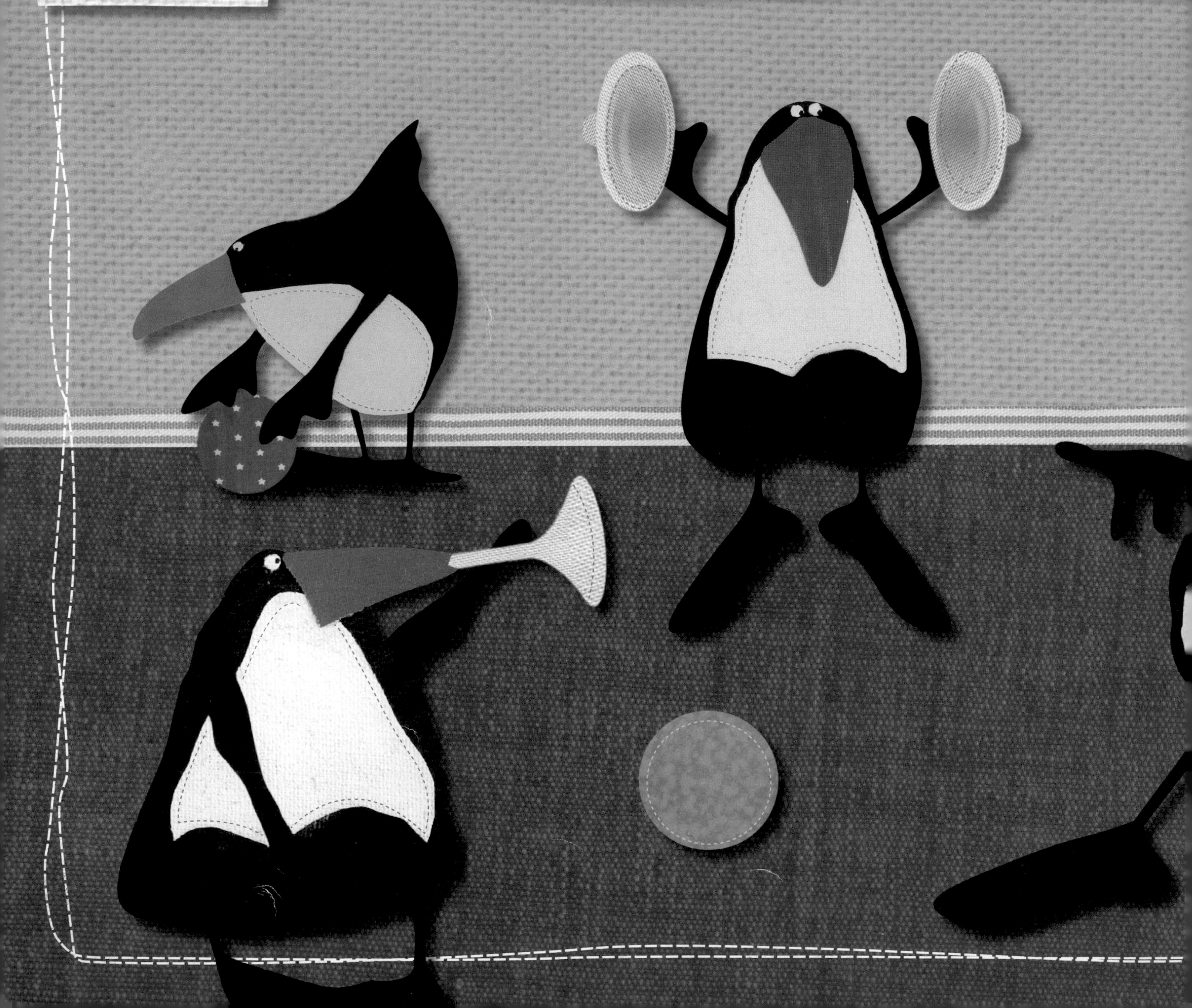

1 of them decides to leave; she doesn't like the noise.

5 quiet penguins watch

but 1 has seen this one before

their favourite show . . .

and thinks it's time to go.

1 cries, "Not sardines!" and jumps

3

funny penguins are

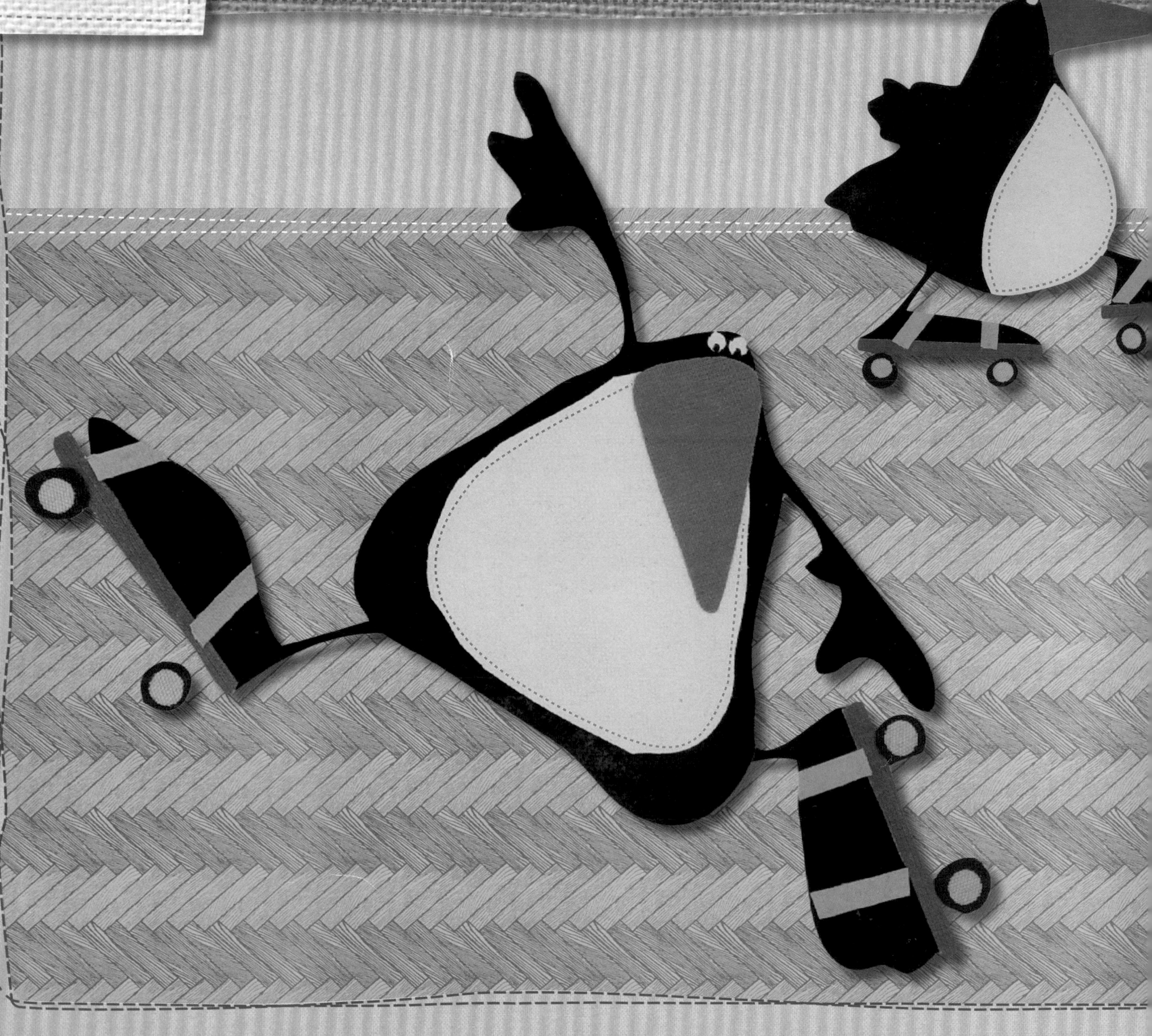

smelly penguins take

Tee hee
Tee hee

She thought her friends